G000161050

Songs of
the Spirit

Compiled by

DAMIAN LUNDY F.S.C.

Kevin Mayhew
Publishers

First published in Great Britain in 1978 by
KEVIN MAYHEW LTD.,
55 Leigh Road,
Leigh-on-Sea, Essex.

ISBN 0 905725 58 1

Printed and bound by E. T. Heron & Co. Ltd., Essex and London.

FOREWORD

For some people the very simple, very popular 'Charismatic ditties' are an obstacle to their acceptance of Renewal. Others love them. I do. But I also appreciate deeply what Brother Damian Lundy and his Group (Lasallian Resource) have done to broaden the music of the Renewal.

At Conferences, like the Priests' at Hopwood ('78), where they have been in charge of the music, we have been helped by what I thought to be a healthy, Catholic balance of folk, traditional and plainsong music.

I have also been delighted by the songs that are their speciality: the Scripture texts they have set to music. The music is tuneful, easy to learn and suited to the mood of the inspired text. I find these songs specially 'songs that you can pray'. So, to judge from the way they sing them, do most other people.

Knowledge of some of these hymns has already spread far, through those who learned them at the Conferences, or heard them on tapes. Start, 'Do not be afraid for I have redeemed you' (Isaiah 43), or 'This then is my prayer' (Ephesians 3) and you find that most know and like it but fumble for the words when they get beyond the refrain.

In 'Songs of the Spirit' Brother Damian has collected and arranged in handy format a balanced variety of the songs and hymns he uses and the ones he has composed. If you look for an emphasis in the collection, it is on Scripture and on praise. In my opinion that emphasis is the right one. I personally welcome this contribution to the music resources of the Renewal.

+ Langton D. Fox
Bishop of Menevia

FOREWORD

INTRODUCTION

Saint Paul wrote to the Christians at Ephesus: 'Be filled with the Spirit. Speak to one another in the words of psalms, hymns and sacred songs. Sing hymns and psalms to the Lord, with praise in your hearts. Always give thanks for everything to God the Father, in the name of our Lord Jesus Christ.' (Ephesians 5)

Paul's enthusiasm speaks persuasively to the Christian communities of today. In recent years, singing has become a more popular and integrated element of Catholic worship - many of us have discovered how music can play a vital role in renewing the life of a parish, school, religious community or prayer-group. It is more than an optional ornament to the liturgy. Singing together is a natural way of celebrating: it breaks down the barriers of shyness and embarrassment which prevent us from opening our hearts to one another and praising God joyfully for his goodness. To experience the power of God's spirit is to be moved to sing out the praises of God our Father and Jesus our Lord. Many Christians have discovered from their contact with charismatic renewal what it means to be liberated from the fears and inhibitions which choke our expression of love and joy. When we hear God's word proclaimed, we need to respond gratefully in our words and actions. Why not, first, in our song?

But do we need another hymnal?

Our communities will, of course, continue to draw on the words and music of 'those who have gone before us, marked with the sign of faith', but what we inherit from them is a living tradition - new songs are constantly being composed, shared, and passed on, in response to the psalmist's call: 'Sing to the Lord a new song'. Songs of the Spirit gathers together some of these new songs.

Many parishes now use the 'Celebration Hymnal', which contains a wide selection of old favourites and popular folk-hymns. With one or two exceptions, I decided to exclude from Songs of the Spirit material included in 'Celebration Hymnal'. I believe most groups will agree with this decision, which means that the new volume can be used alongside standard hymnals or other collections of folk hymns. I have included several hymns which are popular in the Renewal, and a number of previously unpublished hymns, all of which have been tried, tested and approved - and 'duplicated'! Do not be afraid to try out these new songs - they are easy to sing. Helpful demonstration cassettes are available from the publisher. We decided to print two verses of each song under the music, so as to help first-timers.

I believe a good hymn should offer thoughts and images to nourish personal prayer and reflection, as well as being a vehicle of communal praise. The best words and images are scriptural. The music sets the mood of a hymn and so helps to determine the atmosphere of the celebration. Not all songs of the spirit are exuberant alleluias! If we are to praise the Lord at all times, we shall need gentler, meditative music, determined by the demands of the occasion or of the liturgical season.

In editing this collection, I appreciated the help given by many prayer-groups and individuals, who drew my attention to their favourite hymns. I'm grateful to the many British and international publishers who gave permission to include their copyright material, and to Kevin Mayhew for his personal help and encouragement. My thanks to Bishop Langton Fox for his support and kindness in writing a foreword to the hymnal. Most of all I am indebted to my friends who sing these hymns at various liturgical gatherings and renewal conferences, especially those organised at Hopwood Hall. Our group was once nicknamed 'RentaMass', but we prefer to call ourselves 'Lasallian Resource', for everyone either belongs to the De La Salle Brothers or is a close friend and associate of our Lasallian family. In this we are truly a 'band' of brothers (and sisters!). Songs of the Spirit would never have been published without more than a little help from my friends. With love I dedicate it to them.

Damian Lundy, FSC

1 GIFTS OF BREAD AND WINE

Words and Music: Christine McCann

1. Gifts of bread and wine, _____ gifts we've of- fered, _____ fruits of la- bour, _____ fruits of love; _____ ta- ken, of- fered, _____ sanc-ti- fied, blessed and bro- ken; _____ words of one who_ died: 'Take my bo- dy, _____ take my sav- ing blood.'_ Gifts of bread and wine: _____ Christ our Lord. _____

2. Christ our Sa- vi- our, _____ liv- ing pres-ence here_ as he prom- ised _____ while on earth: _____ 'I am with you _____ for all time, I am with you _____ in this bread and_ wine. Take my bo- dy, _____ take my sav- ing blood.'_ Gifts of bread and wine: _____ Christ our Lord. _____

3. Through the Father, with the Spirit,
   one in union with the Son,
   for God's people, joined in prayer
   faith is strengthened by the food we share.
   'Take my body, take my saving blood.'
   Gifts of bread and wine: Christ our Lord.

2. THE LORD IS PRESENT IN HIS SANCTUARY

Words and Music: Gail Cole

1. The Lord is pres-ent in his sanc-tu-a- ry,
2. The Lord is pres-ent in his sanc-tu-a- ry,

let us praise— the Lord. The Lord is pres-ent in his
let us sing to the Lord. The Lord is pres-ent in his

peo- ple gath- ered here, let us praise— the Lord.
peo- ple gath- ered here, let us sing to the Lord.

Praise— him,— praise— him,— let us praise— the
Sing to him,— sing— to him,— let us sing to the

Lord. Praise— him,— praise— him,—
Lord. Sing to him,— sing— to him,—

let us praise— Je- sus!—
let us sing— to Je- sus!—

3. The Lord is present in his sanctuary,
   let us delight in the Lord. (2)
   Delight in him, delight in him,
   let us delight in the Lord. (2)

4. The Lord is present in his sanctuary,
   let us love the Lord. (2)
   Love him, love him,
   let us love the Lord. (2)

3 THE WIND WAS COLD

Words: Damian Lundy. Music: H. J. Richards

1. The wind was cold one April morning,
and the sun was hid in heaven.
They took a man one April morning,
and while he said goodbye,
blew the wind in April.

2. They took a man one April morning,
and the sun was hid in heaven.
They drove the nails into his fingers,
and while he said goodbye,
blew the wind in April.

3. They murdered love one April morning,
and the sun was hid in heaven.
The sky grew black, the rain came falling,
and while he said goodbye,
blew the wind in April. (2)

4. They laid his body in a garden,
and the sun was hid in heaven.
They went away 'til Sunday morning,
and while they said goodbye,
blew the wind in April. (2)

5. The sun shone high on Sunday morning,
yes, the sun shone high in heaven.
He said goodbye, goodbye to sleeping,
and while he said goodbye,
blew the wind in April. (2)

6. And there he stood, one April morning,
and the sun shone high in heaven.
He stood and smiled one April morning,
and when he smiled again,
blew the wind in April. (2)

YOU WHO SLEEP

4

Words and Music: Damian Lundy

Chorus
You who sleep, rise up, al-le-lu-ia. Rise from the dead, rise up, al-le-lu-ia, and Christ shall en-ligh-ten you.

1. You who sleep, rise up with Christ in to his light, al-le-lu-ia. This is the day the Lord has made to dis-pel the night, al-le-lu-lu-ia.

2. Lamb of God, he died to win free-dom for men, al-le-lu-ia. He is the Lord who con-quers death, ri-sing up a-gain, al-le-lu-lu-ia.

3. Christ who died is Lord of life,
   loving and new, alleluia.
   Rise, and his splendid Easter light
   will shine in you, alleluia.

4. Son of man, who lived a life
   death would destroy, alleluia,
   Now you are christened Child of God
   you can shout for joy, alleluia.

5. Christ will come to lead us home;
   he is the way, alleluia.
   He will return; rise up and wait
   for his triumph day, alleluia.

5 SEE HOW THE SKY IS BRIGHT
Words: Damian Lundy. Music: Dutch Folk Melody

1. See how the sky is bright in the morn-ing, then in the
2. Man is a child, a flow'r in the spring-time; Man is a

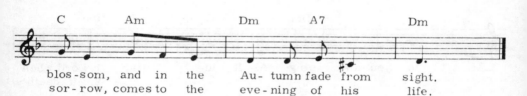

eve - ning dark-ens to night. Flow-ers in Spring-time burst in- to
young man lov-ing a wife; Man is an old man, and af - ter

blos-som, and in the Au- tumn fade from sight.
sor - row, comes to the eve - ning of his life.

3. We have a Father knowing our sorrow,
   giving us bread and caring for us.
   He is our Father, waiting to meet us
   there at the table in his house.

4. We have a Brother knowing our sorrow,
   sharing our bread and sharing our care.
   He was our Brother, dying to save us,
   travelling home to meet us there.

5. We have a Friend who helps us and guides us,
   always unchanging, faithful and true.
   He is the friendship in all our loving,
   oldest and youngest, always new.

6. Lord of our springtime, Lord of our morning,
   Lord, do not leave your people at night!
   If we are weak, Lord, you are unchanging:
   stay with us, keep us in your sight.

7. Lord our God, remember your people:
   Hear us, and when we call to you, come!
   Gather your people as a shepherd;
   Keep us in safety, lead us home.

6 LORD, HOWEVER CAN I REPAY YOU?

Words (based on Psalms 114 and 115): Damian Lundy. Music: R. Jef

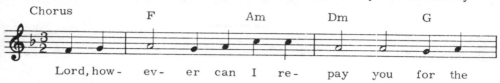

Chorus

Lord, how- ev- er can I re- pay you for the

love you have shown to me? Ev'-ry day I will give thanks

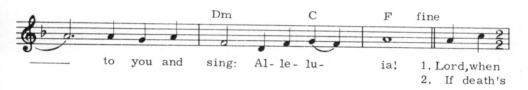

to you and sing: Al- le- lu- ia! 1. Lord, when
2. If death's

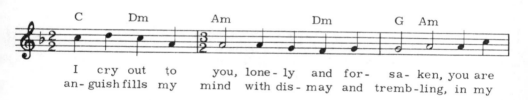

I cry out to you, lone-ly and for- sa-ken, you are
an-guish fills my mind with dis-may and tremb-ling, in my

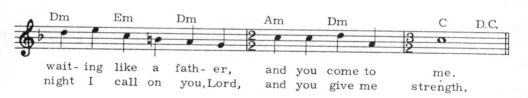

wait-ing like a fath-er, and you come to me.
night I call on you, Lord, and you give me strength.

3. In your justice and your love
   you protect the helpless.
   I was weak, Lord, and you saved me;
   keep me always safe.

4. Lord, you keep my mind in peace,
   and I walk before you,
   trusting in your love and knowing
   you watch over me.

5. Lord, what can I offer you?
   How can I repay you?
   I will raise your saving cup and
   call upon your name.

6. I will tell the world my joy,
   shout it on the rooftops:
   'See our God is wonderful -
   his mercy never ends!'

AVE MARIA

7

Words and Music: Maria Parkinson

1. As I kneel before you, as I bow my head in pray'r, take ___ this day, make ___ it yours and fill me with ___ your love. _____

2. All I have I give you, ev'-ry dream and wish are yours. Mo-ther of Christ, Mo-ther of mine, pre-sent them to ___ my Lord. _____

Chorus*

A -- ve, Ma - ri - a, gra - ti - a ple - na, Do - mi - nus te - cum, be - ne - di - cta tu. _____

* The lower notes are the tune.

3. As I kneel before you,
   and I see your smiling face,
   ev'ry thought, ev'ry word
   is lost in your embrace.

TRANSFIGURATION
8 *Words and Music: Carey Landry*

We be- hold the splen-dour of God
shin- ing on the face of Je- sus. We behold the splen-dour of God shin- ing
on the face of the Son.

1. And oh how his beau- ty trans- forms us, _____
2. Je- sus, Lord _____ of Glo- ry, _____

_____ the won- der of Pres-ence a- bi- ding. _____
_____ Je- sus be- lov-ed Son. _____

Trans-par-ent hearts give re- flec- tion _____ of
Oh _____ how good _____ to be with you; how

C   Bb   F

Ta- bor's light ____ with- in, ____ of
good to share ____ your light, ____ how

C   Bb   F   D.C.

Ta- bor's light with- in. ____
good to share your light. ____

9 COME, LORD JESUS
Words and Music: Sister Rosalie Vissing

This song should be sung slowly and prayerfully. Start softly
and keep getting louder. Improvised harmonies add to the effect.

D   A   D   A

1. Word made flesh, ____ Son of God.
2. Lord and Sa- viour, Son of God.

Chorus G   D   A   D

Come, Lord Je- sus, come a- gain.

G   D   A   D

Come, Lord Je- sus, come a- gain.

3. Prince of Peace, Son of God.

4. Alleluia, Son of God.

5. Bread of Life, Son of God.

6. Light of the World, Son of God.

7. Jesus Christ, Son of God.

GOD AND MAN AT TABLE ARE SAT DOWN

10 *Words and Music: Robert J. Stamps*

1. Wel-come all ye no-ble saints of old, _____ as now be-fore your ve-ry eyes un-fold _____ the won-ders all so long a-go fore-told. _____
2. El-ders, mar-tyrs, all are fal-ling down, _____ proph-ets, pa-tri-archs are gath-'ring round; _____ what an-gels longed to see now man has found. _____

Chorus

God and man at ta-ble are sat down, _____

God and man at ta-ble are sat down. _____

3. Who is this who spreads the vict'ry feast?
   Who is this who makes our waring cease?
   Jesus risen, Saviour, Prince of Peace.

4. Beggars lame, and harlots also here;
   repentant publicans are drawing near;
   wayward sons come home without a fear.

5. Worship in the presence of the Lord
   with joyful songs, and hearts in one accord,
   and let our host at table be adored.

6. When at last this earth shall pass away,
   when Jesus and his bride are one to stay,
   the feast of love is just begun that day.

11 ALLELU!
Words and Music: Mimi Armstrong

1. Come and bless,   come and praise,   come and__ praise the
2. Come and seek,   come and find,   come and__ find the

liv-ing God.   Al-le-lu,   al-le-lu,   al-le-   lu-ia, Je-sus
liv-ing God.   Al-le-lu,   al-le-lu,   al-le-   lu-ia, Je-sus

Chorus

Christ.____   Al- le- lu,   al- le- lu,   al- le- lu- ia,
Christ.____

Je- sus Christ.   Al- le- lu,   al- le- lu,

al- le-   lu- ia, Je- sus   Christ._____

3. Come and hear, come and know,
   come and know the living God.
   Allelu, allelu, alleluia, Jesus Christ.

4. Come and bless, come and praise,
   come and praise the Word of God.
   Word of God, Word made flesh, alleluia, Jesus Christ.

Optional verses
according to season.

5. Come behold, come and see,
   come and see the new-born babe.
   Allelu, allelu, alleluia, Jesus Christ.

6. Angel choirs sing above,
   'Glory to the Son of God.'
   Shepherd folk sing below, 'Allelu, Emmanuel.'

FREELY, FREELY

12 *Words and Music: Carol Owens*

1. God for- gave my sin in Je- sus' name. I've been
2. All pow'r is giv'n in Je- sus' name, in

born a- gain in Je- sus' name. And in Je- sus'
earth and heav'n in Je- sus' name. And in Je- sus'

name I come to you to share his love as he
name I come to you to share his pow'r as he

told me to. He said 'Free- ly, free- ly
told me to.

you have re- ceived; free- ly, free- ly give.

Go in my name, and be- cause you be-

lieve, oth- ers will know that I live. '

13 SING OF A GIRL
Words: Damian Lundy. Music: English Folk Melody

This song for Mary's birthday, and for her presentation (as a child)
in the Temple looks to her future role as Mother of Jesus, so it is
in the future tense - an 'advent' song.

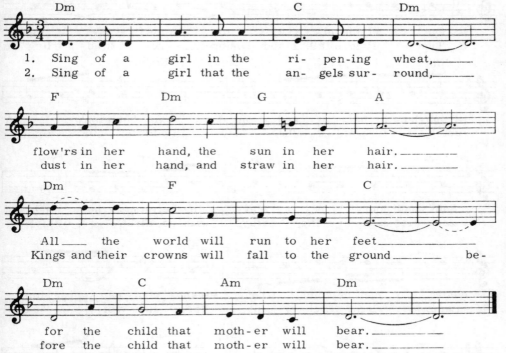

1. Sing of a girl in the ri- pen-ing wheat,
2. Sing of a girl that the an- gels sur- round,

flow'rs in her hand, the sun in her hair.
dust in her hand, and straw in her hair.

All the world will run to her feet
Kings and their crowns will fall to the ground be-

for the child that moth-er will bear.
fore the child that moth-er will bear.

3. Sing of a girl on a hillside alone,
   blood on her hand, and grey in her hair.
   Sing of a body, broken and torn.
   Oh, the child that mother will bear!

4. Sing of the girl a new man will meet,
   hand in his hand, the wind in her hair.
   Joy will rise as golden as wheat
   with the child that mother will bear.

5. Sing of a girl in a circle of love,
   fire on her head, the light in her hair.
   Sing of the hearts the Spirit will move
   to love the child that mother will bear.

6. Sing of a girl who will never grow old,
   joy in her eyes and gold in her hair.
   Through the ages men will be told
   of the child that mother will bear.

14 EMMAUS
Words: Kevin Nichols. Music: Chris O'Brien

1. Out — of the ci — ty in — the first dawn- ing,
troub-led in heart — and mind, two men took — a
Sab- bath jour- ney, leav- ing their hopes— be- hind.
Where— had he come— from, strange com- pan- ion,
sud- den-ly at — their side, as they tramped the
lone- ly high road that qui- et pasch- al tide?

2. Trav- el-lers talk — and hope— re- kind- ling
quick- ly sped— the day. Lights of eve- ning,
dark-ness gath- er- ing; stay— with us, stran- ger, stay!
Lamp- light flick-er- ing, face and voi- ces,
face— of — one— thought dead, ris'n and liv- ing,
sit-ting a-mong— them, known in the break-ing of bread.

3. Hooded traveller, stranger and brother,
sudden unlooked-for friend:
stay with us though the shadows lengthen,
stay 'til the journey's end.
Warmth and welcome, friends and firelight,
and a table spread;
open our eyes and teach us to know you,
Lord, in the breaking of bread.

15 WALK IN THE LIGHT

Words: Damian Lundy. Music: Unknown, arranged by Michael Irwin

1. The Spi- rit lives to set us free, walk, walk
2. Je- sus prom-ised life to all, walk, walk

in the light. He binds us all in u- ni- ty, walk, walk
in the light. The dead were wak-ened by his call, walk, walk

in the light.
in the light.

Chorus
Walk in the light,__ walk in the light,__ walk in the light,__ walk in the light of the Lord.

3. He died in pain on Calvary,
   walk, walk in the light,
   to save the lost like you and me,
   walk, walk in the light.

4. We know his death was not the end,
   walk, walk in the light.
   He gave his Spirit to be our friend,
   walk, walk in the light.

5. By Jesus' love our wounds are healed,
   walk, walk in the light.
   The Father's kindness is revealed,
   walk, walk in the light.

6. The Spirit lives in you and me,
   walk, walk in the light.
   His light will shine for all to see,
   walk, walk in the light.

THE KINTBURY MASS

16 *Words: Damian Lundy. Music: Negro Spiritual (Kyrie);*
R. Jef (Sanctus); Damian Lundy (Agnus Dei)

KYRIE

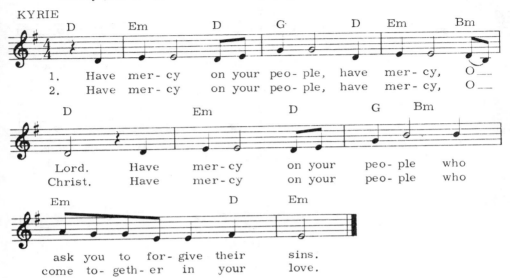

1. Have mer-cy on your peo-ple, have mer-cy, O__
2. Have mer-cy on your peo-ple, have mer-cy, O__

Lord. Have mer-cy on your peo-ple who
Christ. Have mer-cy on your peo-ple who

ask you to for-give their sins.
come to-geth-er in your love.

3. Have mercy on your people,
   have mercy, O Lord.
   Have mercy on your people
   who come to eat the bread of life.

SANCTUS

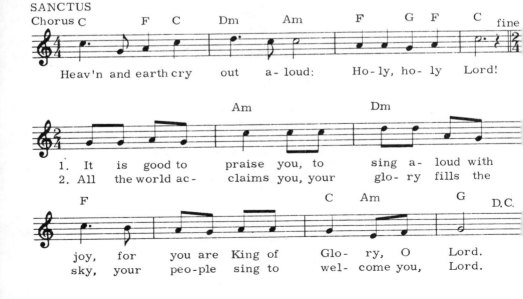

Heav'n and earth cry out a-loud: Ho-ly, ho-ly Lord!

1. It is good to praise you, to sing a-loud with
2. All the world ac- claims you, your glo-ry fills the

joy, for you are King of Glo-ry, O Lord.
sky, your peo-ple sing to wel-come you, Lord.

AGNUS DEI

1. & 2. Lamb of God, you take a-way the sins of our world:

when we ask your mer-cy, hear us, O Lord.

3. Lamb of God, you take a-way the sins of our world:

when we ask for your___ peace, hear us, O Lord.

CHRIST HAS DIED

17 *Music: Joe Wise*

Christ has died,___ al-le-lu-ia.___ Christ is

ri-sen, al-le-lu-ia.___ Christ will

come a-gain,___ al-le-lu-ia, al-le-lu-ia.

18 HE IS LORD!
Words and Music: Unknown

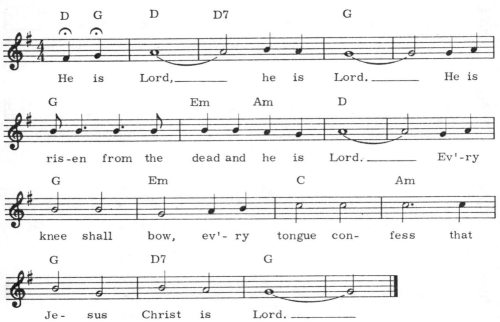

He is Lord,_____ he is Lord._____ He is
ris-en from the dead and he is Lord._____ Ev'-ry
knee shall bow, ev'-ry tongue con-fess that
Je-sus Christ is Lord._____

19 COME, LET US ASCEND
Words (based on Psalm 100) and Music: Mary Barrett

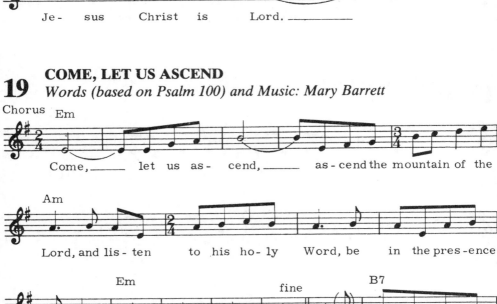

Come,_____ let us as-cend,_____ as-cend the mountain of the
Lord, and lis-ten to his ho-ly Word, be in the pres-ence

of his love._____

1. With joy let all the
2.   Know that he, the

earth cry out, and serve the Lord with glad-ness, come be-
Lord, is God; he made us, we be- long to him, his

Em   B7

fore him._____ With joy let all the
peo- ple. _____ Know that he, the

earth cry out, and serve the Lord with glad-ness, come be-
Lord is God; he made us; we be- long to him, his

Em   B7   Em   B7   D.C.

fore him__ sing-ing for joy._____
peo- ple, the sheep of his flock._____

3. With thanksgiving go within his gates,
   with songs of praise come to his courts
   and bless him.
   With thanksgiving go within his gates,
   with songs of praise come to his courts
   and bless his holy name.

4. The Lord is God, and never-ending
   is his love and mercy.
   He is faithful.
   The Lord is God, and never-ending
   is his love and mercy.
   He is faithful from age to age.

5. Glory to the Father, glory
   to the Son and glory to
   the Spirit.
   Glory to the Father, glory
   to the Son and glory to
   the Spirit, one Lord, one God.

SONG FOR A YOUNG PROPHET
Words (Jeremiah 1) and Music: Damian Lundy

The chorus is sung by the leader and repeated by all at the beginning, and after each verse. The leader sings the verses alone. The final chorus ends on D - all the others ending on F♯.

Chorus

Oh the word of my Lord, _____ deep with-in my be-ing, ____ oh the word of my Lord, _____ you have filled my mind. _____

fine

1. Be - fore I formed you in the womb I knew you through and through, I chose you to be mine. Be - fore you left your moth-er's side I called to you, my child, to be my sign.

2. I know that you are ve-ry young, but I will make you strong - I'll fill you with my word; and you will tra-vel through the land, ful-fil-ling my com-mand which you have heard.

3. And ev'rywhere you are to go
   my hand will follow you;
   you will not be alone.
   In all the danger that you fear
   you'll find me very near,
   your words my own.

4. With all my strength you will be filled:
   you will destroy and build,
   for that is my design.
   You will create and overthrow,
   reap harvests I will sow
   - your word is mine.

21 THE BEATITUDES
Words (based on Matthew): James Quinn. Music: Noel Donnelly

Blest are you, o poor in spi- rit; here is wealth be-yond all tel- ling. Blest are you that faint with hun- ger; here is food all want dis- pel- ling. Blest are you that weep for sor- row; end- less glad- ness here is giv- en. Blest are you when men shall hate you; I will be your

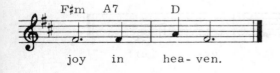

joy in hea- ven.

22 OUR FATHER I
Music: Francesca Leftley

23 YOU ARE NEAR

Words (based on Psalm 139) and Music: Dan Schutte

Chorus
Yah-weh, I know you are near, standing always at my side. You guard me from the foe and you lead me in ways ever lasting.

1. Lord, you have searched my heart, and you know when I sit and when I stand. Your hand is upon me, protecting me from death, keeping me from harm.

2. When can I run from your love? If I climb to the heavens, you are there. If I fly to the sunrise or sail beyond the sea, still I'd find you there.

3. You know my heart and its ways,
   you who formed me before I was born,
   in secret of darkness, before I saw the sun,
   in my mother's womb.

4. Marvellous to me are your works;
   how profound are your thoughts, my Lord!
   Even if I could count them, they number as the stars,
   you would still be there.

THE NIGHT BEFORE OUR SAVIOUR DIED

24 *Words: Damian Lundy. Music: Gerard Markland*

Joyfully

1. The night be-fore___ our Saviour died,___ he took a loaf___ of bread. He blessed it, broke___ it, gave it to___ his friends be-side___ him, and he said: 'Take this___ and eat, it, do, my bo-dy now___ for you.___ Take this___ and eat, it, do, my bo-dy now___ for you.'___

2. And tak-ing then___ a cup of wine, ___ he of-fered thanks___ a-gain, and gave it to___ his friends to drink___ in mem'-ry of___ his com-ing pain. 'This is ___ my blood,' he said, 'for you it will___ be shed.___ This is___ my blood,' he said, 'for you it will___ be shed.'___

3. And so today his brothers meet,
   remembering the night
   on which our Saviour gave himself
   to be our food, to be our light,
   to be our unity,
   the bread of charity. (Repeat)

4. Lord, send your Spirit into us
   and make us one, we pray.
   Make us your body and your blood,
   your presence in the world today.
   Take us and share us, do,
   your body now for you. (Repeat)

5. Lord Jesus, present in our meal,
   be with us all the day,
   in all the people that we meet,
   in everything we do and say.
   And our life will be yours,
   and your life will be ours. (Repeat)

25 KEEP IN MIND
Words and Music: Lucien Deiss

This may be used as a Eucharistic acclamation. Since this song is not
suitable for guitar, it is suggested that organ or piano accompaniment
is used.

Chorus

Keep in mind that Je-sus Christ has died for us and is

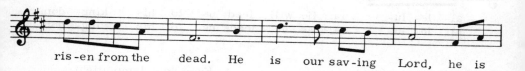

ris-en from the dead. He is our sav-ing Lord, he is

joy for all a-ges. 1. If we die with the
2. If we en-dure with the

Lord, we shall live with the Lord.
Lord, we shall reign with the Lord.

3. In him all our sor-row, in him all our joy.
4. In him hope of glo-ry, in him all our love.

5. In him our redemption,
   in him all our grace.

6. In him our salvation,
   in him all our peace.

26 WHEN THE LORD RETURNS
Words: Damian Lundy. Music: Traditional English Children's Song

An Advent song for children - adults may join in!

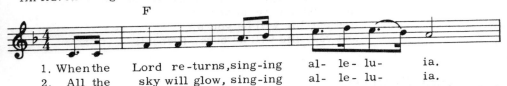

1. When the Lord re-turns, sing-ing al- le- lu- ia.
2. All the sky will glow, sing-ing al- le- lu- ia.

al-le-lu- ia, al- le-lu- ia! He will lead us home, sing-ing
al-le-lu- ia, al- le-lu- ia! All the earth will shake sing-ing

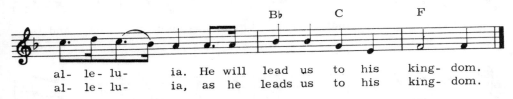

al- le- lu- ia. He will lead us to his king- dom.
al- le- lu- ia, as he leads us to his king- dom.

3. He will come as king,
   singing alleluia..!
   Rise and welcome him,
   singing alleluia.
   He will lead you to his kingdom.

4. Keep your lamp alight,
   singing alleluia..!
   Stay awake and watch,
   singing alleluia.
   He will lead you to his kingdom.

5. Come, Lord Jesus, come,
   singing alleluia..!
   Come and lead us home,
   singing alleluia.
   Come and lead us to your kingdom.

27 LORD, HAVE MERCY
Words (based on Ezechiel) and Music: Gerard Markland

Chorus

Lord, have mer- cy. Lord, have mer- cy.

Lord, have mer-cy on your peo-ple. ___

Lord, have mer-cy. Lord, have mer- cy.

Lord, have mer-cy on your peo-ple. ___

1. Give me the heart of stone with- in you, ; ___
2. You'll find me near the bro- ken- hearted: ___

and I'll give you a heart of flesh.
those crushed in spi- rit I will save.

Clean wa- ter I will use to cleanse all your wounds.
So turn to me, ___ for my par- don is great;

My Spi- rit I give to you.
my word will heal all your wounds.

C7♭9

28 I AM THE WAY

Words (based on Saint John): Mary Barrett.
Music: Mary Barrett and Eileen Binding

Chorus

Je- sus, you are Lord. _____ You are
ri- sen from the dead and you are Lord. _____ Ev'- ry __
knee shall bow, and ev'- ry tongue con- fess that
Je- sus, you are Lord. You are the way. *fine*

1. I _____ am the Way. _____ No one knows the Fa- ther
2. I _____ am the Truth. _____ And I set my spi- rit

but it be through me. _____ I am in my Fa-
deep with- in your hearts, _____ and you will know

ther, and my Fa- ther is in me, and we come in love to
me, and __ love _____ me, and the truth I give to

live with- in your hearts. _____
you will set you free. _____

3. I am the Life.
   The living waters I pour out for you.
   Anyone who drinks of the waters that I give
   will have eternal life.

4. I am the Word,
   the true light that shines brightly in the dark,
   a light that darkness could not overpower,
   The Word made Flesh, risen among you.

Because of their irregular metre, the four verses should be
sung by a soloist. Everyone responds in the chorus.

OUR GOD REIGNS
29
Words and Music: Leonard E. Smith, Jr.

How love-ly on the moun-tains are the
feet of him _____ who brings good news, _____ good
news, _____ an-nounc-ing peace, pro- claim-ing news of
hap- pi- ness: _____ Our God reigns, _____ our God
reigns, _____ our God reigns, _____ our God reigns, _
_____ our God reigns, _____ our God reigns!

30 I HEARD THE LORD
Words and Music: Jacob Krieger

1. I heard the Lord call my name; lis-ten close, you'll hear the same! I heard the Lord call my name; lis-ten close you'll hear the same! I heard the Lord call my name; lis-ten close, you'll hear the same! Take his hand, we are glo-ry bound!

2. His Word is love, love's his word, that's the mes-sage that I heard! His Word is love, love's his word, that's the mes-sage that I heard! His Word is love, love's his word, that's the mes-sage that I heard! Take his hand, we are glo-ry bound!

Verses 2 and 4 only

Place your hand in his and you will know! He will show you where to go!

3. I felt his love from above
   settle on me like a dove. (3)
   Take his hand; we are glory bound!

4. And to the Father all your days
   with the Son and Spirit praise! (3)
   Take his hand; we are glory bound!
   Place your hand in his and you will know;
   he will show you where to go.

5. Repeat verse 1.

ALL GLORY TO YOU
31 *Words: Damian Lundy. Music: R. Jef*

The verses should be sung by a leader, with everyone
thundering in at the chorus!

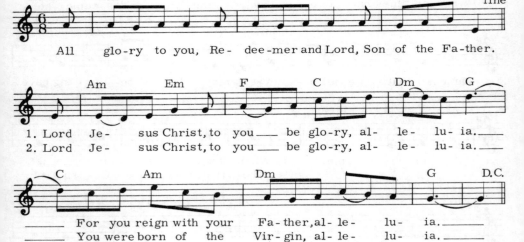

Chorus Am   F   C   Dm   Em fine

All glo-ry to you, Re- dee-mer and Lord, Son of the Fa-ther.

Am   Em   F   C   Dm   G

1. Lord Je- sus Christ, to you ___ be glo-ry, al- le- lu- ia.___
2. Lord Je- sus Christ, to you ___ be glo-ry, al- le- lu- ia.___

C   Am   Dm   G   D.C.

___ For you reign with your Fa-ther, al- le- lu- ia.___
___ You were born of the Vir- gin, al- le- lu- ia.___

3. Lord Jesus Christ, to you be glory, alleluia.
   You fought evil and conquered, alleluia.

4. Lord Jesus Christ, to you be glory, alleluia.
   Risen Lord, we acclaim you, alleluia.

5. Lord Jesus Christ, to you be glory, alleluia.
   You have ransomed God's people, alleluia.

6. Lord Jesus Christ, to you be glory, alleluia.
   You have made us God's children, alleluia.

7. Lord Jesus Christ, to you be glory, alleluia.
   Lead us all to your kingdom, alleluia.

JESUS TO THE RESCUE

32 *Words: Alan Johnson, H. J. Richards and friends. Music: Alan Johnson*

This is a 'catechetical' song, composed at a family weekend. There is a light-hearted, popular flavour to the words and tune which appeal strongly to children; but, underlying this is a deep scriptural theology. The verses should be sung by a narrator, with everyone joining in the chorus.

Chorus

Je-sus to the res-cue! Sev-en times to the res-cue!

Sev-en times he told you and me why he came; he

came so that we all be-liev-ers may be, and be-liev-ing have

life in his name.
1. When John, the ev-an-gel-ist,
2. The first time in Ca-na of

was an old man the Christ-ians were hav-ing it
Ga-li-lee, a bride and a bride-groom felt

rough: ____ 'O where and O where has our Sa-viour
blue ____ be-cause all they'd got was some wa-

gone? Of ____ wait-ing we've had quite e-nough!! ____ So
ter, so he gave them a far bet-ter brew. ____ And

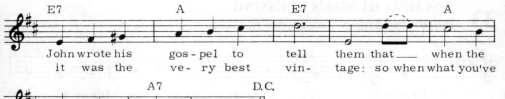

John wrote his   gos - pel   to   tell   them that ___ when the
it   was   the   ve - ry best   vin-   tage: so when what you've

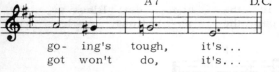

go- ing's   tough,   it's...
got   won't   do,   it's...

3. Then there was the case of the nobleman
   whose son lay a-dying one day.
   His father said: 'Cure him or else he'll die!'
   Said Jesus: 'Go home. He's O.K.'
   Dad smiled when they said: 'The lad's better.
   So when death is on the way, it's...

4. There was at the Sheep Gate a healing pool,
   with a cripple who just couldn't cope;
   for thirty-eight years he'd been crowded out,
   he never could get down the slope.
   But Jesus said: 'Pick up your mat, mate!'
   So when you've lost all hope, it's...

5. The next sign again up in Galilee,
   a great crowd had followed him there.
   When supper-time came, they could only find
   five loaves and two fishes to share.
   Said Jesus: 'Don't worry, I'll fix it.'
   So when the cupboard's bare, it's...

6. Some sailors were having it rough in a storm,
   when approaching them over the sea,
   to everyone's fright came a ghostly shape,
   who said: 'Take it easy, it's me!'
   They suddenly saw it was Jesus:
   so when you're scared as can be, it's...

7. There once was a man who was blind from birth,
   he could not tell a shrimp from a shark,
   and Jesus put mud on his eyes and said:
   'Go wash in the pond in the park.'
   And when he had washed, he said: 'Blimey!'
   So when you're in the dark, it's...

8. The last sign was given in Bethany
   where Lazarus died in his bed.
   When Jesus arrived, he was four days late,
   but he went to the tomb and he said:
   'Why worry? I'm your Resurrection!'
   So when you're feeling dead, it's...

33 ANCIENT RUSSIAN BLESSING
Words and Music: Traditional Russian

1. Praise to God___ in the high- est! Bless us, O
2. Guide and pros- per the na- tions, ru- lers and

Fa- ther! Praise to ___ you!
peo- ples. Praise to ___ you!

3. May the truth in its beauty flourish triumphant.

4. May the mills bring us bread for food and for giving.

5. May the good be obeyed and evil be conquered.

6. Give us laughter and set all your people rejoicing.

7. Peace on earth and good will be ever among us.

34 COME AND WORSHIP
Words and Music: Unknown

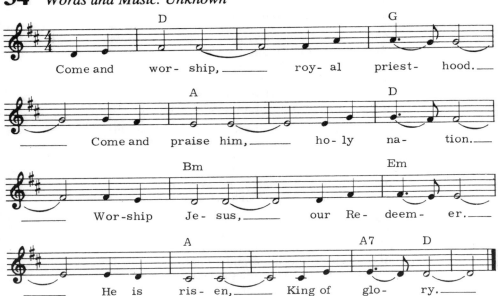

Come and wor- ship, ___ roy- al priest- hood. ___

___ Come and praise him, ___ ho- ly na- tion. ___

___ Wor- ship Je- sus, ___ our Re- deem- er. ___

___ He is ris- en, ___ King of glo- ry. ___

FEAR NOT, REJOICE AND BE GLAD

35

Words and Music: Priscilla Wright

Chorus

Fear not, re-joice and be glad, the Lord hath done a great thing; hath poured out his Spi-rit on all man-kind,— on those who con-fess his name.—

1. The fig tree is bud-ding, the vine bear-eth fruit, the wheatfields are gol-den with grain.— Thrust in the sick-le, the har-vest is ripe, the Lord— has giv-en us rain.—

2. Ye shall eat in plen-ty and be sa-tis-fied, the mountains will drip with sweet wine.— My chil-dren shall drink of the foun-tain of life, my children will know they are mine.—

3. My people shall know that I am the Lord,
   their shame I have taken away.
   My Spirit will lead them together again,
   my Spirit will show them the way.

4. My children shall dwell in a body of love,
   a light to the world they will be.
   Life shall come forth from the Father above,
   my body will set mankind free.

SING ALLELUIA!
36 *Words and Music: Unknown*

1. Sing al- le- lu- ia, sing al- le- lu- ia,
2. Fa- ther, I thank you, Fa- ther, I thank you,

sing al- le- lu- ia. You are my Lord.
Fa- ther, I thank you. You are my Lord.

3. Jesus, I love you. . .

4. Spirit, I need you. . .

5. Sing alleluia. . .

In another version of this hymn each verse is
addressed to Jesus:

1. Jesus, I love you. . .

2. Jesus, I thank you. . .

3. Jesus, I praise you. . .

4. Jesus, I trust you. . .

HAIL, MARY
37 *Music: Estelle White*

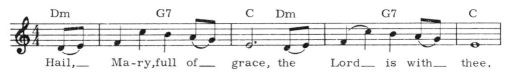

Hail,__ Ma-ry, full of__ grace, the Lord__ is with__ thee.

Blessed art thou among wo- men and bless-ed is the fruit of thy womb,

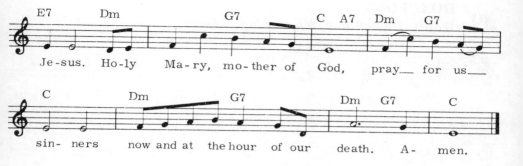

Je-sus. Ho-ly Ma-ry, mo-ther of God, pray__ for us__ sin-ners now and at the hour of our death. A- men.

DO NOT BE AFRAID

38 *Words (based on Isaiah 43: 1-4) and Music: Gerard Markland*

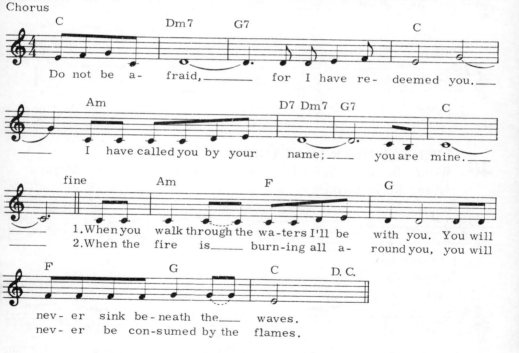

Chorus

Do not be a- fraid,_____ for I have re- deemed you.__ I have called you by your name;____ you are mine.__

fine

1. When you walk through the wa-ters I'll be with you. You will
2. When the fire is__ burn-ing all a- round you, you will

nev- er sink be-neath the__ waves.
nev- er be con-sumed by the flames.

3. When the fear of loneliness is looming,
   then remember I am at your side.

4. When you dwell in the exile of the stranger,
   remember you are precious in my eyes.

5. You are mine, O my child; I am your Father,
   and I love you with a perfect love.

39 DOXOLOGY
Words: Thomas Ken. Music: Jimmy Owens

Praise God ___ from ___ whom all bles - sings flow, praise him, ___ all crea - tures here ___ be - low. Praise him ___ a- bove, ye hea - ven- ly host. Praise Fa- ther, Son, and Ho- ly Ghost.

40 LIKE THE DEER THAT THIRSTS FOR WATER
Words (based on Psalm 41): Luke Connaughton and Kevin Mayhew
Music: Kevin Mayhew

1. Like the deer ___ that yearns for wa- ter, O ___ God, I long for you. Weep-ing I ___ have heard them taunt me: 'What ___ help is in your God?'
2. Glad- ly I ___ would lead your peo- ple, re- joic- ing to your house. Trust in God, ___ my soul, and praise him, and ___ he will dry your tears.

3. Grief and pain, like roaring torrents,
   had swept my soul away.
   But his mercy is my rescue,
   I will praise him all my days.

4. Weeping, I have heard them taunt me:
   'What help is in your God?'
   Rock of strength, do not forget me,
   In you alone I trust.

5. To the Father praise and honour,
   all glory to the Son,
   honour to the Holy Spirit:
   let God be glorified.

41 MOTHER OF GOD'S LIVING WORD
Words: Damian Lundy. Music: P. de Corbeil (13th century)

1. Moth- er   of God's liv- ing Word, glo- ri-   fy- ing
2. Vir- gin soil, un- touched by   sin,   for God's seed to

Christ your Lord; full of joy, God's peo- ple sing,
flour- ish   in;   wa- tered by the   Spi- rit's dew

grate- ful for your moth- er- ing.
in your womb the Sa- viour grew.

3. Sharing his humility
   Bethlehem and Calvary,
   with him in his bitter pain,
   now as queen with him you reign.

4. We are God's new chosen race,
   new-born children of his grace,
   citizens of heaven who
   imitate and honour you.

5. We, God's people on our way,
   travelling by night and day,
   moving to our promised land,
   walk beside you hand in hand.

6. Christ, your Son, is always near,
   so we journey without fear,
   singing as we walk along:
   Christ our joy, and Christ our song!

7. Sing aloud to Christ with joy
   who was once a little boy!
   Sing aloud to Mary, sing,
   grateful for her mothering.

42 AS LONG AS MEN

Words: Huub Oosterhuis and C. M. DeVries.
Music: Portuguese Folk Melody

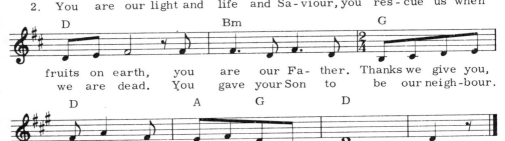

1. As long as men on earth are liv-ing, and trees are yield-ing fruits on earth, you are our Fa-ther. Thanks we give you, for all that owes to you its birth._____
2. You are our light and life and Sa-viour, you res-cue us when we are dead. You gave your Son to be our neigh-bour. He feeds us with his liv-ing bread._____

3. As long as human words are spoken
   and for each other we exist,
   your steadfastness remains unbroken;
   for Jesus' sake, your name be blessed.

4. You are the one who clothes the flowers,
   you feed the birds in all the land.
   You are our shelter: all my hours
   and all my days are in your hand.

5. Therefore, let all the world adore you.
   It is your love that brought it forth.
   You live among us, we before you.
   Your offspring are we. Praise the Lord!

43 HOW GOOD IT IS TO KNOW YOUR NAME

Words: Damian Lundy. Music: Breton Folk Melody

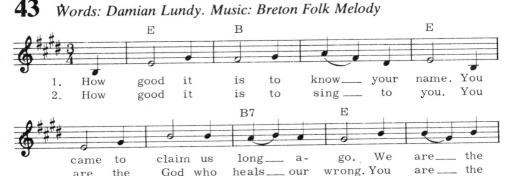

1. How good it is to know____ your name. You came to claim us long____ a-go. We are____ the
2. How good it is to sing ____ to you. You are the God who heals____ our wrong. You are____ the

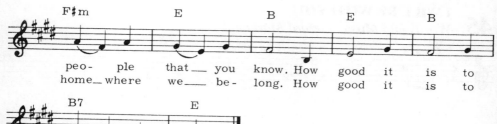

peo- ple that __ you know. How good it is to
home __ where we __ be - long. How good it is to

know __ your name.
sing __ to you.

3. How good it is to find you near.
   We are the seed - you make us grow.
   You are the leaven, we the dough.
   How good it is to find you near.

4. How good it is to sing to you.
   You are the bread that makes us strong.
   You are the reason for our song.
   How good it is to sing to you.

44 PRAISE THE LORD WITH DANCING!
Words and Music: Mary Barrett

1. Praise the Lord with danc- ing! __ Praise the Lord with
2. Praise him, hills and moun- tains! __ Praise him trees and

Chorus

sing-ing! __ Praise the Lord, __ oh my soul! Oh my
for-ests! __

soul, __ praise the Lord!

3. Praise him, highest heavens!   4. Praise him, kings and peoples!
   Praise him, deepest waters!   Praise him, all you rulers!

5. Praise God in his temple!
   Praise him, highest heaven!

45 I WILL BE WITH YOU
Words and Music: Gerard Markland

3. Your life will be transformed with power
   by living truly in my name.

4. And if you say: 'Yes, Lord, I love you,'
   then feed my lambs and feed my sheep.

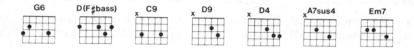

IN YOUR COMING AND GOING

46 *Words (based on Psalm 120): Damian Lundy. Music: D. Julien*

Chorus

In your com- ing and go- ing God is with you. He will
keep you in safe- ty night and day. fine

1. You raise your
2. His arm out-

eyes and you look at the moun- tains; you cry a-
stretched to pro- tect you in dan- ger, he nev- er

loud to the hills: 'Come and help__ me!' Now, see our
sleeps all the time he is watch- ing. He is the

God is on his way; he will stay be- side you night and day.
ma- ker of the skies, but he knows your name, he hears your cries.

3. His loving care shelters you like a shadow,
   to keep you safe from the evil around you.
   He shields you from the burning sun,
   and the moon at night will do no harm.

THE HOPWOOD MASS

47 *Words: Terence Collins, F.S.C. Music: Welsh Melody adapted by Terence Collins, F.S.C. and David Bentley*

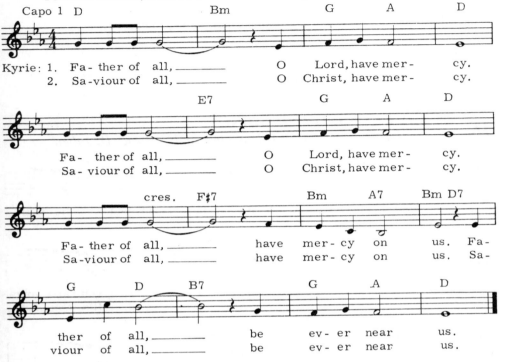

3. Spirit of all, O Lord, have mercy.
   Spirit of all, O Lord, have mercy.
   Spirit of all, have mercy on us.
   Spirit of all, be ever near us.

SANCTUS
1. Holy are you, Lord of creation!
   Holy are you, Lord God of angels!
   Holy are you, God of all people!
   Heaven and earth proclaim your glory.

2. Glory to you! Your name is holy.
   Blessed is he who comes in your name!
   Glory to him! We sing his praises.
   Heaven and earth, cry out Hosanna!

AGNUS DEI
O Lamb of God, you bore our sinning.
O Lamb of God, you bore our dying.
O Lamb of God, have mercy on us.
O Lamb of God, your peace be with us.

MAGNIFICAT

48 *Words (based on the Magnificat):Unknown. Music:Scottish Folk Melody*

1. My__ soul is filled with joy__ as I sing to God my
2. I am low-ly as a child,__ but I know from this day

Sa-viour: he has looked up-on his ser-vant, he has
for-ward that my name will be re- mem-bered,for all

vi- si-ted his peo-ple. **Chorus** And __ ho- ly is his
men will call me bles-sed.

name through__ all ge-ne- ra-tions! Ev-er- last-ing is his

mer-cy to the peo- ple he has cho-sen, and__

ho- ly is his name!

3. I proclaim the pow'r of God!
   He does marvels for his servants;
   though he scatters the proud-hearted
   and destroys the might of princes.

4. To the hungry he gives food,
   sends the rich away empty.
   In his mercy he is mindful
   of the people he has chosen.

5. In his love he now fulfills
   what he promised to our fathers.
   I will praise the Lord, my saviour.
   Everlasting is his mercy.

ANNUNCIATION CAROL

49

Words: S. Baring-Gould. Music: Basque Folk Melody

1. The an- gel, Ga- bri- el, from hea- ven
came,_____ his wings as drif- ted snow, his eyes_____
_____ as flame._____ 'All hail, 'said he, 'thou low- ly
mai- den, Ma- ry,_____ most high- ly
fa- voured la- dy. ' Glo-_____
ri- a!_____

2. For know, a bless- sed Moth- er thou shall
be!_____ All ge- ne- ra- tions laud and hon-
_____ our thee._____ Thy Son shall be Em- man- u-
el, by seers fore- told,_____ most high- ly
fa- voured la- dy. ' Glo-_____
ri- a!_____

3. Then gentle Mary meekly bowed her head.
'To me be, as it pleaseth God, ' she said.
'My soul shall laud and magnify his holy name! '
Most highly favoured lady! Gloria!

4. Of her, Emmanuel, the Christ, was born
in Bethlehem, all on a Christmas morn;
and Christian folk throughout the world will ever say:
'Most highly favoured lady! ' Gloria!

50 THE LOURDES MAGNIFICAT
Words: Lesbordes. Music: Abbé P. Decha

Chorus

God_ fills me_ with _ joy, al-le-lu- ia. His_ ho-ly

pres-ence is my robe, al-le-lu- ia. 1. My soul, now
2. The world shall

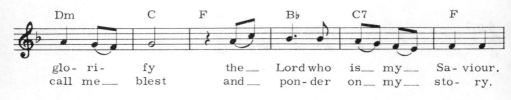

glo-ri- fy the_ Lord who is_ my_ Sa-viour.
call me_ blest and_ pon-der on_ my_ sto-ry.

Re- joice, for who_ am_ I, that God has
In me is ma- ni- fest God's great-ness

shown_ me_ fa- vour.
and _ his_ glo- ry.

3. For those who are his friends
and keep his laws as holy
his mercy never ends,
and he exalts the lowly.

4. But by his power the great,
the proud, the self-conceited,
the kings who sit in state
are humbled and defeated.

5. He feeds the starving poor,
he guards his holy nation,
fulfilling what he swore
long since in revelation.

6. Then glorify with me
the Lord who is my Saviour:
one holy Trinity
for ever and for ever.

I AM THE BREAD OF LIFE

51 *Words and Music: Sister Suzanne Toolan, S.M.*

1. I am the bread of life. He who comes to me shall not

hun-ger. He who be-lieves in me shall not thirst. No-one can come to

me un- less the Fa- ther draw him.

Chorus

And I will raise ___ him up, ___ and I will raise ___ him

up, ___ and I will raise ___ him up ___ on the last ___ day.

2. The bread that I will give is my flesh for the life of the

world, ___ and he who eats of this bread, he shall live for

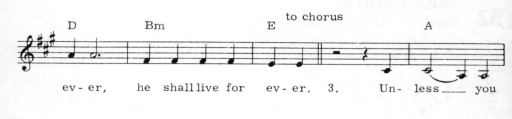

to chorus

ev - er, he shall live for ev - er. 3. Un - less___ you

eat of the flesh of the Son of Man, and drink of his blood, and

to chorus

drink of his blood, you shall not have life with - in you.

4. I am the re - sur - rec - tion, I am the life.___ He who be -

to chorus

lieves___ in me, ev - en if he die, he shall live for ev - er.

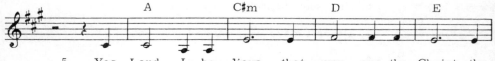

5. Yes, Lord, I be - lieve that you are the Christ, the

to chorus

Son___ of God, who___ has come in - to the world.

52 ABBA, FATHER
Words and Music: Rosalie Vissing

The verses in this song should be sung by a small group.
Everyone sings the chorus.

1. Ab- ba, Fa- ther, send your Spi- rit. Glo- ry, Je- sus
2. I will give you liv- ing wa- ter. Glo- ry, Je- sus

Christ. Ab- ba, Fa-ther, send your Spi- rit. Glo- ry, Je-sus
Christ. I will give you liv- ing wa- ter. Glo- ry, Je-sus

Christ. Glo-ry hal-le- lu- jah, glo-ry, Je-sus Christ.
Christ.

Glo- ry hal-le- lu- jah, glo- ry, Je- sus Christ.

3. If you seek me you will find me.

4. If you listen you will hear me.

5. Come, my children, I will teach you.

6. I'm your shepherd, I will lead you.

7. Peace I leave you, peace I give you.

8. I'm your life and resurrection.

9. Glory Father, glory Spirit.

Other words from Scripture may be substituted according to the occasion or
the season. For example, in Advent: 1. Come, Lord Jesus, Light of nations.
2. Come, Lord Jesus, born of Mary.
3. Come, and show the Father's glory.

53 O MARY, WHEN OUR GOD CHOSE YOU
Words: Damian Lundy. Music: Swiss Folk Melody

The last two lines of each verse should be repeated.

2. When he was born on Christmas night
   and music made the rafters ring,
   the stars were dancing with delight;
   now all God's children sing.

3. One winter's night, a heap of straw
   becomes a place where ages meet,
   when kings come knocking at the door
   and kneeling at your feet.

4. In you, our God confounds the strong
   and makes the crippled dance with joy;
   and to our barren world belong
   his mother and her boy.

5. In empty streets and broken hearts
   you call to mind what he has done;
   where all his loving kindness starts
   in sending you a son.

6. And Mary, while we stand with you,
   may once again his Spirit come,
   and all his brothers follow you
   to reach our Father's home.

54 FATHER, I PLACE INTO YOUR HANDS
Words and Music: J. Hewer

1. Fa-ther, I place in- to your hands the things that I can't do. Father, I place in- to your hands the times that I've been through. Fa-ther, I place in- to your hands the way that I should go, for I know I al- ways can trust you.

2. Fa-ther, I place in- to your hands my friends and fa- mi- ly. Father, I place in- to your hands the things that trou- ble me. Fa-ther, I place in- to your hands the per- son I would be, for I know I al- ways can trust you.

3. Father, we love to seek your face,
   we love to hear your voice.
   Father, we love to sing your praise,
   and in your name rejoice.
   Father, we love to walk with you
   and in your presence rest,
   for we know we always can trust you.

4. Father, I want to be with you
   and do the things you do.
   Father, I want to speak the words
   that you are speaking too.
   Father, I want to love the ones
   that you will draw to you,
   for I know that I am one with you.

FOR YOU ARE MY GOD

55 *Words (based on Psalm 16) and Music: John Foley, S.J.*

Chorus

For you are my God, _____ you a- lone are my
joy. _____ De- fend me, O Lord. _____

1. You give mar- vel- lous com- rades to me: _____
   the faith- ful who dwell in your land. _____
2. You are my por- tion and cup; _____
   it is you that I claim for my prize. _____

Those __ who choose a- li- en gods _____
Your he- ri- tage is my de- light, _____

have cho- sen an a- li- en band. _____
the lot you have giv- en to me. _____

3. Glad are my heart and my soul;
   securely my body shall rest.
   For you will not leave me for dead,
   nor lead your beloved astray.

4. You show me the path for my life;
   in your presence the fullness of joy.
   To be at your right hand for ever
   for me would be happiness always.

56 O MY PEOPLE

Words (based on the Good Friday 'Reproaches') and Music: Damian Lundy

Since this song is not suitable for guitar, it is suggested that organ or piano accompaniment is used.

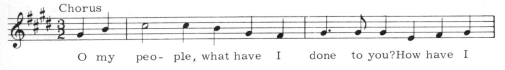

O my peo- ple, what have I done to you? How have I

hurt you? An-swer me. 1. I led you out of E-
          2. I led you as a shep-

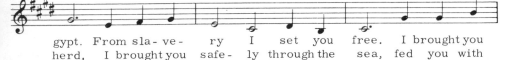

gypt. From sla- ve- ry I set you free. I brought you
herd, I brought you safe- ly through the sea, fed you with

in- to a land of prom- ise; you have pre- pared a cross for
man- na in the des- ert; you have pre- pared a cross for

me.
me.

3. I fought for you in battles,
   I won you strength and victory,
   gave you a royal crown and sceptre:
   you have prepared a cross for me.

4. I planted you, my vineyard;
   and cared for you most tenderly,
   looked for abundant fruit, and found none
   - only the cross you made for me.

5. Then listen to my pleading,
   and do not turn away from me.
   You are my people: will you reject me?
   For you I suffer bitterly.

GLORIA

57 *Words and Music: Francesca Leftley*

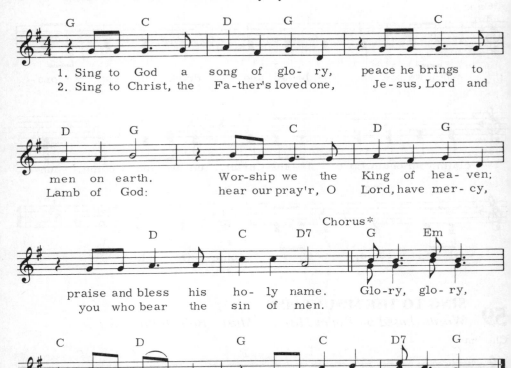

1. Sing to God a song of glory,
   peace he brings to men on earth.
   Worship we the King of heaven;
   praise and bless his holy name.

2. Sing to Christ, the Father's loved one,
   Jesus, Lord and Lamb of God:
   hear our pray'r, O Lord, have mercy,
   you who bear the sin of men.

Chorus*

Glory, glory, sing his glory.
Glory to our God on high.

* The lower notes are the melody.

3. Sing to Christ, the Lord and Saviour,
   seated there at God's right hand:
   hear our pray'r, O Lord, have mercy,
   you alone the Holy One.

4. Glory sing to God the Father,
   glory to his only Son,
   glory to the Holy Spirit,
   glory to the three in one.

WHEN WE EAT THIS BREAD

58 *Music: Joe Wise*

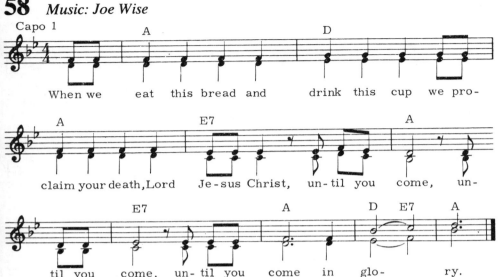

When we eat this bread and drink this cup we proclaim your death, Lord Je-sus Christ, un-til you come, un-til you come, un-til you come in glo-ry.

SING TO THE MOUNTAINS

59 *Words (based on Psalm 118) and Music: Bob Dufford, S.J.*

Chorus

Sing to the moun-tains, sing to the sea. Raise your voi-ces, lift your hearts. This is the day the Lord has made. Let all the earth re-joice.

1. I will give thanks to you, my Lord. You have

THE LIGHT OF CHRIST

60 *Words and Music: Donald Fishel*

Chorus

The light of Christ has come into the
The light of Christ has come in-

world, the light of Christ has
to the world, the light of Christ

come in- to the world.
has come.

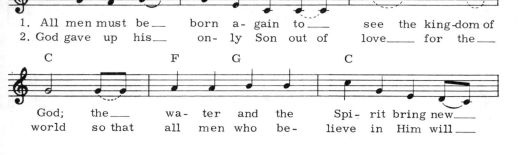

1. All men must be born a- gain to see the king-dom of
2. God gave up his on- ly Son out of love for the

God; the wa- ter and the Spi- rit bring new
world so that all men who be- lieve in Him will

Dm   G   D.C.

life___ in God's love.___
live___ for___ ev- er.

F   C

3. The light of God has___ come to us so that

F   G   C   F   G

we might have sal- va- tion; from the dark-ness of our

C   Dm   G   D.C.

sins we walk in- to glo- ry with Christ Je- sus.

FATHER, WE ADORE YOU

61 *Words and Music: Terrye Coelho*

This song may be sung as a round.

1 G   Am   D   G   2   Am

1. Fa- ther, we a- dore you, lay our lives be-
2. Je- sus, we a- dore you, lay our lives be-

D   G   3   Am   D   G

fore you. How we love you.
fore you. How we love you.

3. Spirit, we adore you...

62 AN EASTER CAROL

Words (based on a French poem): Damian Lundy. Music Polish Carol

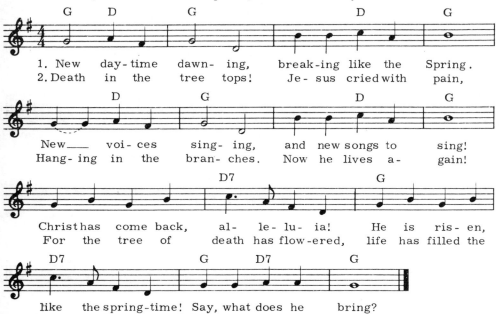

1. New day-time dawn-ing, break-ing like the Spring.
   New___ voi-ces sing-ing, and new songs to sing!
   Christ has come back, al-le-lu-ia! He is ris-en,
   like the spring-time! Say, what does he bring?

2. Death in the tree tops! Je-sus cried with pain,
   Hang-ing in the bran-ches. Now he lives a-gain!
   For the tree of death has flow-ered, life has filled the
   furth-est bran-ches! Sun-light fol-lows rain.

3. The man of sorrows,
   sleeping in his tomb,
   the man of sorrows,
   he is coming home.
   He is coming like the springtime.
   Suddenly you'll hear him talking,
   you will see him come.

4. Say are you hungry?
   Come and eat today!
   Come to the table,
   nothing to pay!
   Take your place, the meal is waiting.
   Come and share the birthday party,
   and the holiday.

5. Look where the garden
   door is open wide!
   Come to the garden,
   there's no need to hide.
   God has broken down the fences
   and he stands with arms wide open.
   Come along inside!

COME, HOLY SPIRIT

63 *Words: Psalm 103. Music: Ernest Sands.*

Come, Ho-ly Spi-rit, fill the hearts of your faith-ful, and

light up in them the fire of your love.

Send out your Spi-rit and they shall be cre- a- ted, and

you will re- new the face of the earth.

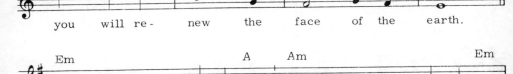

1. Bless the Lord, my soul.   Lord God, how great you are.
2. How many are your works, O Lord;   in wisdom you have made them all.

Clothed in majes- ty and glory, wrapped in light as in a robe.
The earth is full of your riches, living things great and small.

3. You hide your face, they are dismayed,
   you take back your Spirit, they die.
   You send forth your Spirit, they are created,
   and you renew the face of the earth.

4. I will sing to the Lord all my life,
   make music to my God while I live.
   May my thoughts be pleasing to him;
   I find my joy in the Lord.

64 IF GOD IS FOR US

Words (based on Romans 8:31-39) and Music: John Foley, S.J.

The chorus is sung rhythmically, not too fast. The verses should be sung
faster by a leader or small group.
The melody is the lower notes. Chords in brackets should be played on Capo 3.

Chorus

F (D)   Gm (Em)   C (A)

If God is for__ us, who can be a-gainst,

F (D)   Gm (Em)   C (A)   F

____ if the Spi-rit of God has set us free?__

Gm (Em)   C (A)

If God is for__ us, who can be a-gainst,

F (D)   Gm (Em)   C (A)   F (D)

____ If the Spi-rit of God has set us free?__

fine   Eb (C)   Bb (G)   F (D)

1. I know that noth-ing in this world
2. Noth-ing can take us from his love,

Eb (C)   Bb (G)   C (A)   C7 (A7) D.C.

can ev-er take us from his__ love.____
poured out in Je-sus, the__ Lord.____

3. And nothing present or to come
   can ever take us from his love.

4. I know that neither death nor life
   can ever take us from his love.

65 OH! HOW GOOD IS THE LORD

Words and Music: Traditional arranged by Elaine Irwin

Chorus

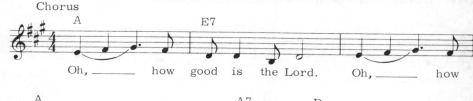

Oh, ____ how good is the Lord. Oh, ____ how

good is the Lord. Oh, ____ how good is the Lord! I

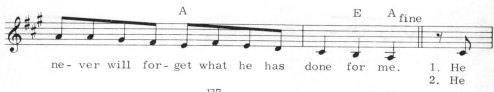

ne - ver will for - get what he has done for me. 1. He
2. He

gives us sal - vation. How good is the Lord. He gives us sal - vation. How
gives us his Spi - rit how good is the Lord. He gives us his Spi - rit, how

good is the Lord. He gives us sal - va - tion. How good is the Lord. I
good is the Lord. He gives us his Spi - rit, how good is the Lord.

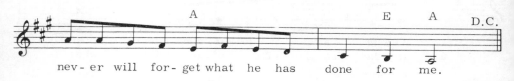

nev - er will for - get what he has done for me.

3. He gives us his healing...

4. He gives us his body...

5. He gives us his freedom...

6. He gives us each other...

7. He gives us his glory...

ROMANS 8

66 *Words (based on Romans 8:28-38) and Music: Enrico Garzilli*

us from the love of Christ? Neith-er trou-ble,___ nor
us from the love of Christ? Not the past, ___ the

pain,___ nor per-se- cu-tion.___
pres- ent, nor the fu- ture.___

67 THIS IS THE DAY
Words: Unknown. Music: Fiji Folk Melody

1. This is the day, this is the day that the Lord has made, that the
2. This is the day, this is the day when he rose a- gain, when he

Lord has made.
rose a- gain. We will re-joice, we will re-joice and be

glad in it, and be glad in it. This is the day that the
This is the day when he

Lord has___ made.
rose a- gain. We will re-joice and be glad in___ it.

This is the day that the Lord has made.
This is the day when he rose a- gain.

3. This is the day when the Spirit came...

68 I WILL SING, I WILL SING
Words and Music: Max Dyer

2. We will come, we will come as one before the Lord. (3)
   Alleluia, glory to the Lord.

3. If the Son, if the Son shall make you free, (3)
   you shall be free indeed.

4. They that sow in tears shall reap in joy. (3)
   Alleluia, glory to the Lord.

5. Ev'ry knee shall bow and ev'ry tongue confess (3)
   that Jesus Christ is Lord.

6. In his name, in his name we have the victory. (3)
   Alleluia, glory to the Lord.

This song is most effective when sung without
accompaniment, but with light clapping.

69 BIND US TOGETHER

Words and Music: Unknown. Lyrics revised and music arranged by Michael Irwin

Chorus

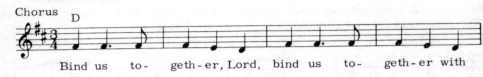

Bind us to- geth- er, Lord, bind us to- geth- er with

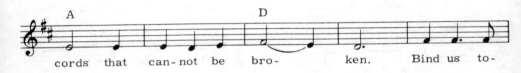

cords that can- not be bro- ken. Bind us to-

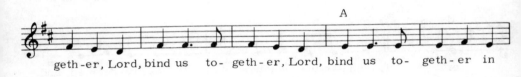

geth- er, Lord, bind us to- geth- er, Lord, bind us to- geth- er in

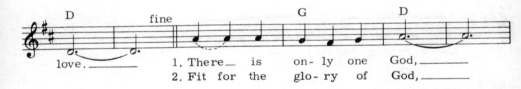

love. _____ 1. There___ is on- ly one God, _____
2. Fit for the glo- ry of God, _____

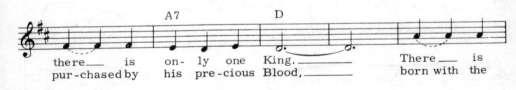

there___ is on- ly one King. _____ There___ is
pur-chased by his pre-cious Blood, _____ born with the

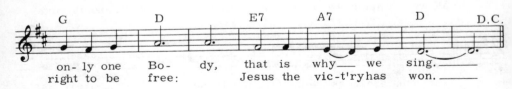

on- ly one Bo- dy, that is why___ we sing. _____
right to be free: Jesus the vic-t'ry has won. _____

3. We are the fam'ly of God,
   we are his promise divine,
   we are his chosen desire,
   we are the glorious new wine.

70 ALABARE

Words and Music: Unknown

'Alabaré a mi Senor' means 'Praise to my Lord'. This hymn has become a favourite at international conferences. The chorus is always sung in Spanish. The final verse may be improvised to suit the occasion.

Chorus

A-la-ba- re,— a-la-ba- re, a- la-ba-re a mi Sen-

or. A-la-ba- re,— a-la-ba- re, a- la-ba-re a mi Sen-

or. 1. John saw the num-ber of all those re-deemed, and

all were sing-ing prai-ses to the Lord.

Thousands were pray-ing, ten thous-ands re-joic-ing, and

all were singing praises to the Lord. 2. There is no

god as great as you, O Lord, there is none, there is

none. There is no none. There is no god who does the mighty

REMEMBER, MARIA

71

Words (based on the 'Memorare') and Music: Christine McCann

Chorus

Re- mem-ber, Ma- ri- a, re- member, Ma- ri- a, the

pray'rs of your chil- dren, their trust in __ you. Re-

mem-ber, Ma- ri- a, re- member, Ma- ri- a, as we come be-

fore you, our trust __ in __ you. *fine*

1. God's chil- dren re-
2. Dear Ma- ry, our

1. mem-ber you, Ma- ry, so mild. Your __ Son is the
2. moth- er, your chil- dren are told of your mer- cy and

1. Lord by whom we're re- con- ciled. God's love is with
2. good- ness re- nowned from of old. God's Spi- rit is

1. you, heal- ing us of our sin. So __ o- pen your
2. with you: in ev'- ry em- brace God smiles in your

1. arms, __ draw us __ gent- ly __ in.
2. eyes; __ we see __ him in __ your __ face.

D.C.

3. In sorrow and pain we continue to come;
   draw us closer to Christ, to our brother, your Son.
   Remember the needs of our world as we pray:
   Be near us to comfort your children each day.

72 MAGNIFICAT
Words (based on the Magnificat):Unknown. Music:American Folk Melody

1. My___ soul pro-tions claims the Lord my
2. All na-tions now will share my

God, my___ spi-rit___ sings his___ praise!___
joy, his gifts he has out-poured;

___ He___ looks on___ me, he lifts me
his lit-tle ones he has made

up, and___ glad-ness___ fills my days.___
great; I mag-ni-fy the Lord.

3. His mercy is for evermore!
   His name I praise again!
   His strong right arm puts down the proud
   and raises lowly men!

4. He fills the hungry with good things,
   the rich he sends away.
   The promise made to Abraham
   is filled by him each day.

5. Magnificat, magnificat,
   magnificat, praise God!
   Magnificat, magnificat,
   magnificat, praise God!

73 FOLLOW ME
Words: Michael Cockett. Music: Sister Madeleine, F.C.J.

Chorus

Fol-low me, fol-low me, leave your home and fa-mi-
ly, leave your fish-ing nets and boats up-on the shore.——
—— Leave the seed that you have sown, leave the crops that you've
grown, leave the peo-ple you have known and fol-low me.——

1. The fox-es have their holes and the swal-lows have their
2. If you would fol-low me, you must leave old ways be-

nests, but the Son of man has no place to lay down.——
hind. You must take my cross and fol-low on my path.——

—— I do not of-fer comfort, I do not of-fer
You may be far from loved ones, you may be far from

wealth, but in me will all hap-pi-ness be found.————
home but my Fa-ther will wel-come you at last.————

3. Although I go away
   you will never be alone,
   for the Spirit will be
   there to comfort you.
   Though all of you may scatter,
   each follow his own path,
   still the Spirit of love will lead you home.

ALLELUIA NO.1
74 *Words and Music: Donald Fishel*

Al- le- lu- ia, al- le- lu- ia, give___ thanks to the

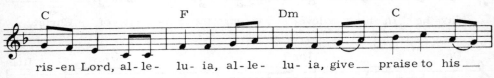

ris-en Lord, al- le- lu- ia, al- le- lu- ia, give___ praise to his___

name.　1. Je- sus is Lord of all the___ earth.
　　　 2. Spread the good news all o'er the___ earth.

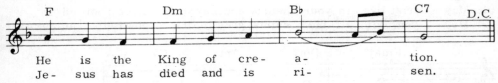

He　is　the　King　of　cre- a-   tion.
Je- sus has died and is ri-   sen.

3. We have been crucified with Christ.
   Now we shall live for ever.

4. God has proclaimed the just reward:
   life for all men, alleluia.

5. Come, let us praise the living God,
   joyfully sing to our Saviour.

EPHESIANS 3

75 *Words (based on Ephesians 3:14-21): Damian Lundy.*
Music: Gerard Markland

The chorus is not sung after verse 3.

Chorus

This, then, is my pray'r, fal-ling on my knees be-

fore God who is Fath-er and source of all life.___

May he in his love, through the Spi- rit of Christ,

give you pow'r to grow strong in your in- ner-most self.___

1. May Christ live in your hearts and may your lives, root-ed in
2. May you, with all the saints, grow in the pow'r to un-der-

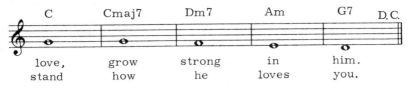

love, grow strong in him.
stand how he loves you.

3. O how can I explain
in all its depth and all its scope
his love, God's love!

4. For his love is so full,
it is beyond all we can dream:
his love, in Christ!

5. And so, glory to him
working in us, who can do more
than we can pray!

Cmaj7

SPIRIT OF THE LIVING GOD
76 *Words and Music: Daniel Iverson*

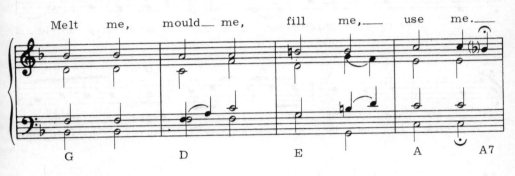

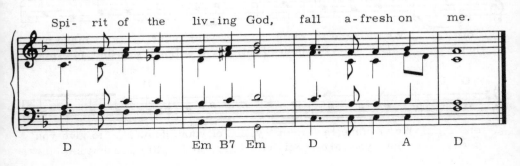

PLEASE BREAK THIS BREAD, LORD

77 *Words and Music: Jodi Page*

Chorus

Please— break this bread, Lord,— please break this bread,—

—— bread of your bo- dy—— ri-sen in us.

Pour out your wine, Lord, pour out your wine.——

last time

—— Let it flow through us —— to a thirst-y world.——

1. We've come to eat —— your bread, —— make us
2. Let us be bro-ken, —— O Lord, —— to feed your

one.—— We've come to drink —— your wine, —— make us
sheep.—— Let us be poured out, —— O Lord, —— that men may

one.—— We've come in mem'ry—— of your death —— to give you
see—— that you are Spi- rit —— and life —— that sat- is-

thanks:___ We've come to ce-le-brate___ your life___ and give you
fy,___ that you are

praise. ris-en___ in us___ to set men___ free.___

Please break this bread, Lord,___ please break this bread.___

Pour out your wine, Lord, pour out your wine.

78 YOUR WORD IS MY LIGHT
Words and Music: Gerald O'Mahony

Your Word is my light, my lamp, my way, my

lan-tern by night, my com-pass by day. Your

Word is my light, my lamp, my way, your

Word is a lan-tern for me.___

79 SEEK YE FIRST
Words and Music: Karen Lafferty

This may be sung as a round.

1. Seek ye__ first the__ King- dom of God, and his__ righteous-
2. Ask and it shall be giv-en un-to you, seek and ye shall

ness, and all these things shall be add-ed un- to you;
find; knock and it shall be op-ened un- to you;

al- le- lu, al-le- lu- ia. Al- le- lu- ia, al- le-
al- le- lu, al-le- lu- ia.

lu- ia, al- le- lu- ia, al- le- lu, al-le- lu- ia.

This second verse is not part of the song as
originally written. The origin is unknown.

80 MY SOUL IS LONGING FOR YOUR PEACE
Words (based on Psalm 131) and Music: Lucien Deiss

Since this song is not suitable for guitar, it is suggested that organ or
piano accompaniment is used.

My soul is long-ing for your peace, near to you, my God.

1. Lord, you know that my heart is not proud, and my eyes are
2. Loft- y thoughts have nev-er filled my mind, far be- yond my

not lift- ed from the earth.
sight all am- bi-tious deeds.

3. In your peace I have maintained my soul,
   I have kept my heart in your quiet peace.

4. As a child rests on his mother's knee,
   so I place my soul in your loving care.

5. Israel, put all your hope in God,
   place your trust in him, now and evermore.

THE SONG OF RUTH
81 *Words and Music: Gerald O'Mahony*

Chorus

Wherev-er you go___ I will go, wherev-er you live___ I will live. Your peo-ple shall be my peo-ple, and your God shall be my God.___

fine

1. Now is the time for you to
2. Each bird that flies will have its

go back to the land you used to know,
nest. You, Je-sus, have no place to rest,

but I will go with you; that I may be with you;
but I will go with you; that I may be with you;

I'll fol-low you through wind and rain and snow.
with you my rest-less heart is hea-ven blest.

ABBA, FATHER IN HEAVEN

82 *Words (based on the Lord's Prayer) and Music: Patrick Geary*

Ab-ba, Fa-ther in __ hea-ven, hal-lowed be __ your __

name. Your __ king-dom come, your will be done on earth as it is in

hea-ven. Give us to-day our dai-ly __ bread and for-

give __ us our sins, as we for-give __ our __ broth-ers. And

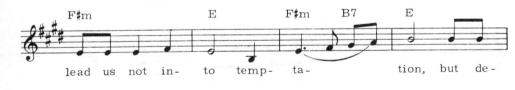

lead us not in-to temp-ta- tion, but de-

li-ver us from ev-il. A- men. For the

king-dom, the pow'r and the glo-ry are yours; now and for

ev- er, now___ and for ev- er.

NOW THE GREEN BLADE RISETH

83 *Words: J. M. C. Crum. Music: French Folk Melody*

1. Now the green blade ris - eth from the__ bur- ied grain,
2. In the grave they laid him, love whom men had slain,

wheat that in the dark earth ma- ny__ days has lain;
think- ing that nev- er he would wake a- gain,

love lives a- gain, that with the dead has been:
laid in the earth like grain that sleeps un- seen:

love is come a- gain like wheat that__ springeth green.
love is come a- gain like wheat that__ springeth green.

3. Forth he came at Easter, like the risen grain,
   he that for three days in the grave had lain;
   quick from the dead my risen Lord is seen:
   love is come again like wheat that springeth green.

4. When our hearts are wintry, grieving or in pain,
   thy touch can call us back to life again;
   fields of our heart that dead and bare have been:
   love is come again like wheat that springeth green.

ONE COLD NIGHT IN SPRING

84 *Words and Music: Damian Lundy*

1. One cold night in Spring the wind blew strong.
   Then the darkness had its hour.
   A man was eating with his friends,
   for he knew his death was near.

2. And he broke a wheaten loaf to share,
   for his friends a last goodbye.
   'My body is the bread I break.
   Oh, my heart will break and die!'

3. Then he poured good wine into a cup,
   blessed it gently, passed it round.
   'This cup is brimming with my blood.
   Soon the drops will stain the ground.'

4. See a dying man with arms outstretched
   at the setting of the sun.
   He stretches healing hands to you.
   Will you take them for your own?

5. Soon a man will come with arms outstretched
   at the rising of the sun.
   His wounded hands will set you free
   if you take them for your own.

85 ABBA, FATHER
Words and Music: Carey Landry

Chorus

Ab - ba, _____ Ab - ba, Fa-ther, _____ You are the pot- ter, _____ we are the clay, _____ the work of your hands. _____

1. Mould us, _____ mould us and fash- ion us _____ in- to the im- age _____ of Je-sus, your Son, _____ of Je-sus, your Son. _____

2. Fa- ther, _____ may we be one in you _____ as he is in _____ you _____ and you are in him _____ and you are in him. _____

3. Glory, glory and praise to you,
   glory and praise to you
   for ever, amen,
   for ever, amen.

Chorus: All   fine

Al- le- lu- ia, ___ al- le- lu- ia, ___ al- le- lu- ia.

Cantor

Easter: Lord Je- sus, you are ri-sen from the dead; you are our com-

pan-ion on the road of life, and we know ___ you in the breaking

D.C.

of the bread.

2. **For Advent and Christmas**

> Lord Jesus, Word of God made man for us,
> you reveal your glory to our broken world,
> and we worship you. Come again in glory!

3. **For Passiontide**

> Lord Jesus, obedient to the Father's will,
> you became a slave, enduring death for us.
> Now you reign as Lord. Come again in glory!

4. **For Pentecost**

> Lord Jesus, you are at the Father's side:
> you have sent your Spirit to renew our joy,
> and we praise you. Come again in glory!

87 LAY YOUR HANDS GENTLY UPON US
Words and Music: Carey Landry

Chorus

Lay your hands gent-ly up- on us, _____ let their

touch ren-der your peace, _____ let them bring your for-

give-ness and heal-ing, _____ lay your hands gent-ly, lay your

hands. _____
fine
1. You were sent to free the bro- ken
2. Lord, we come to you through one a-

heart-ed. _____ You were sent to give sight to the
no- ther. _____ Lord, we come to you in all our

blind. _____ You de- sire to heal all our ill- ness.__
need. _____ Lord, we come to you seek-ing whole-ness._

_____ Lay your hands, gent-ly lay your hands. _____
D.C.
_____ Lay your hands gent-ly lay your hands. _____

A hymn for Christian unity, appropiate for ecumenical occasions and penitential services, as well as for Maundy Thursday.

1. Lord Je-sus Christ, up- on the night of your great ag- on-
2. Lord Je-sus Christ, we pray that in your good-ness you will

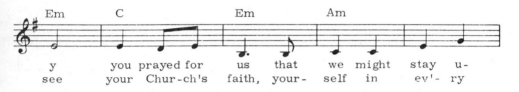

y   you prayed for   us   that   we might   stay u-
see   your Chur-ch's   faith, your- self   in   ev'- ry

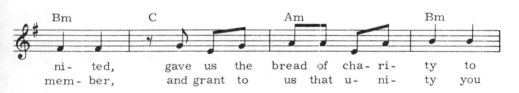

ni- ted,   gave us the   bread of cha- ri-   ty   to
mem- ber,   and grant to   us that u- ni-   ty   you

share as bro-thers   to one   meal___ in-   vi- ted.
prayed for on   the   night we now___ re-   mem- ber.

3. Lord Jesus Christ, we pray that in your love you will not see
   our lack of faith, our sins against our neighbour.
   Pardon our infidelity.
   Lord, hear our Church's pray'r, and bless her labour.

4. Lord Jesus Christ, on your divided Church look graciously,
   give her your peace and end all separations,
   that we may live fraternally;
   grant that your peace may reign among all nations.

VENI CREATOR SPIRITUS

Words: attributed to Rabanus Maurus (766-856). Music: Plainsong

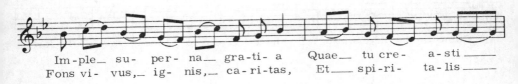

1. Ve-ni, Cre- a-tor— Spi-ri-tus, Men-tes tu- o-rum— vi- si- ta
2. Qui di-ce- ris Pa- ra-cli-tus, Al-tis-si-mi do- num De- i,

Im-ple— su- per- na— gra-ti- a Quae— tu cre- a-sti—
Fons vi- vus,— ig- nis,— ca-ri-tas, Et— spi-ri- ta-lis—

pec-to- ra. A- men.—
un- cti- o.

3. Tu septiformis munere,
   Digitus paternae dexterae,
   Tu rite promissum Patris.
   Sermone ditans guttura.

4. Accende lumen sensibus,
   Infunde amorem cordibus,
   Infirma nostri corporis
   Virtute firmans perpeti.

5. Hostem repellas longius,
   Pacemque dones protinus:
   Ductore sic te praevio,
   Vitemus omne noxium.

6. Per te sciamus, da, Patrem,
   Noscamus atque Filium,
   Teque utriusque Spiritum
   Credamus omni Tempore.

7. Deo Patri sit gloria,
   Et Filio, qui,a mortuis
   Surrexit, ac Paraclito,
   In saeculorum saecula.

90 COME, COME, FOLLOW ME

Words (based on Matthew 6) and Music: Mary Barrett

Chorus

Come, come, fol-low me! Come and see where I live!

Come and see what I shall give to those who fol-low

me._____

1. Look at the gras-ses of____ the field:____
2. Look at the ra-vens gloss-y and sleek:____

_____ they neith-er spin, nor do they weave, yet ev-en
_____ they neith-er sow, nor do they reap,____ they____

Sol- o- mon was not like these, when dressed in
do not store good things to eat, yet God feeds them

all his glo- ry.
from his boun- ty.

3. Look at the sparrows so small and light:
not one is forgotten in God's sight.
So rejoice in his love and take delight:
you are worth more than hundreds of sparrows.

4. So don't frét about your bódies
or hów you are to dréss:
if you cánnot clothe the flówers
why thínk about the rést?
For Gód, in his wísdom,
will províde what is bést
for the líttle flock of his kíngdóm.

THE SPIRIT IS MOVING

91 *Words and Music: Unknown, arranged by Michael Irwin*

1. All ov-er the world ____ the Spi-rit is mov-ing, all ov-er the world ____ as the proph-ets said it would be. All ov-er the world ____ there's a migh-ty re-ve-la-tion of the glo-ry of the Lord, as the wa-ters cov-er the sea. ____

2. All ov-er this land ____ the Spi-rit is mov-ing, all ov-er this land ____ as the proph-ets said it would be. All ov-er this land ____ there's a migh-ty re-ve-la-tion of the glo-ry of the Lord, as the wa-ters cov-er the sea. ____

3. All over the church...

4. All over us all...

5. Deep down in my heart...

EIGHT-FOLD ALLELUIA
Words and Music: Traditional

Verses are sung according to the occasion. For example:

3. Abba, Father...

4. Holy Spirit...

or

3. And I love him...

4. Send your Spirit...

93 ALL THE EARTH PROCLAIM THE LORD
Words (based on Psalm 100) and Music: Lucien Deiss

Since this song is not suitable for guitar, it is suggested that organ or piano accompaniment is used.

Chorus

All the earth pro- claim— the Lord, sing your praise to

God.   1. Serve you the Lord, heart filled with glad- ness. Come
        2. Know that the Lord is our cre- a- tor. Yes,

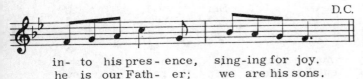

in- to his pres- ence, sing-ing for joy.
he is our Fath- er; we are his sons.

3. We are the sheep of his green pasture,
   for we are his people; he is our God.

4. Enter his gates bringing thanksgiving,
   O enter his courts while singing his praise.

5. Our Lord is good, his love enduring,
   his Word is abiding now with all men.

6. Honour and praise be to the Father,
   the Son, and the Spirit, world without end.

94 OH LORD MY GOD
Words: Michael Cockett. Music: Sister Madeleine

Oh Lord my God, the Fa-ther of cre- a- tion,
Chorus: For you are Lord, your love is high as hea-ven.

to you I turn when I am most a- fraid.
You are as faith- ful as the clouds a- bove.

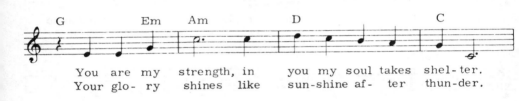

You are my strength, in you my soul takes shel- ter.
Your glo- ry shines like sun-shine af- ter thun-der.

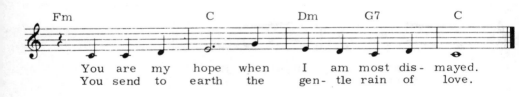

You are my hope when I am most dis- mayed.
You send to earth the gen- tle rain of love.

2. Oh Lord my God, the hope of all creation.
   You are the star that guides me on my way.
   Awake in me the music of the future;
   you teach the song, and I will sing and play.

3. Oh Lord my God, the love in all creation,
   you are the one to teach me how to care.
   You set me free to learn to love my brother;
   let me, through love, my faithfulness declare.

95 I WILL SING A SONG

Words (based on Psalm 146): Damian Lundy. Music Joseph Gelineau

I will sing a song, a song to please our God, a

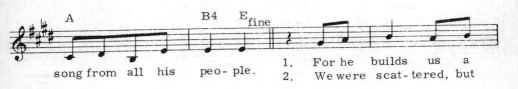

song from all his peo- ple.

1. For he builds us a
2. We were scat-tered, but

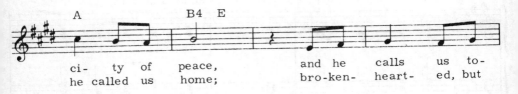

ci- ty of peace, and he calls us to-
he called us home; bro-ken- heart- ed, but

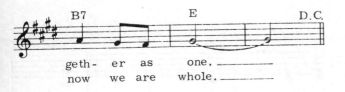

geth- er as one. _____
now we are whole. _____

3. We are healed - he has bound up our wounds,
   he who calls all the stars by their names.

4. He is God of the world that he made,
   he is God of the poor that he helps.

5. How he covers the heavens with clouds!
   How he clothes mountain valleys with green!

6. He sends food to young ravens in need.
   He will come if you wait for his love.

7. To the Father and Son sing a song,
   to the Spirit who fills us with life.

96 HALLELUJAH, MY FATHER
Words and Music: Tim Cullen

Recommended to be sung in parts, without accompaniment!

With quiet devotion

Hal - le - lu - jah, my__ Fa__ ther,__ for__

giv - ing us your Son; send - ing him__ in-

to__ the world__ to be giv - en up for men,

know - ing__ we would bruise him__ and smite him from __ the

earth. Hal-le- lu- jah, my__ Fa- ther,__ in his

death__ is my birth.__ Hal-le- lu- jah, my__

Fa- ther,__ in his life__ is my life._____

97 OUR FATHER II
Music: Estelle White

we for-give those who tres-pass against us and lead us not in-to temp-

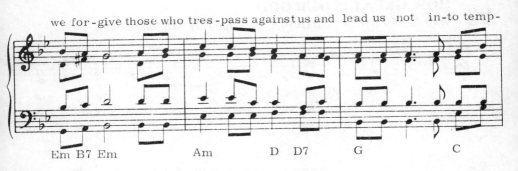

Em B7 Em   Am   D   D7   G   C

ta- tion,   but de-   li-   ver us from   ev-   il.

G   G7   C   G

Doxology

     For the   king- dom, the power and the   glo- ry   are

     yours,   now   and for   ev-   er.

HOW GREAT IS OUR GOD

98 *Words and Music: Unknown, arranged by Michael Irwin*

1. How great is our God, _____ how great is his
2. How great is our God, _____ how great is his

name! _____ How great is our God, _____ for- ev- er the
name! _____ How great is our God, _____ for- ev- er the

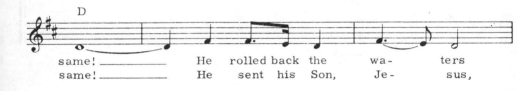

same! _____ He rolled back the wa- ters
same! _____ He sent his Son, Je- sus,

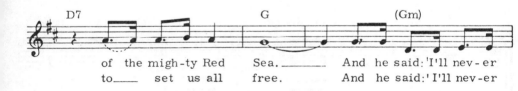

of the migh-ty Red Sea. _____ And he said: 'I'll nev-er
to____ set us all free. And he said: 'I'll nev-er

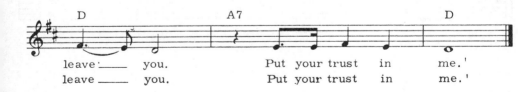

leave ____ you. Put your trust in me.'
leave ____ you. Put your trust in me.'

3. How great is our God,
   how great is his name!
   How great is our God,
   for ever the same!
   He gave us his Spirit, and now we can see.
   And he said: 'I'll never leave you.
   Put your trust in me.'

99 I WILL NEVER FORGET YOU

Words (based on Isaiah 49:15) and Music: Carey Landry

100 OUR FATHER III
Music: Unknown, arranged by Michael Irwin

A lovely 'echo' effect is obtained in this setting - everyone just follows the leader.

Leader: Our Fa - ther, _____ who art in heav'n, _____ hal-lowed

All: Our Fa - ther, _____ who art in heav'n, _____

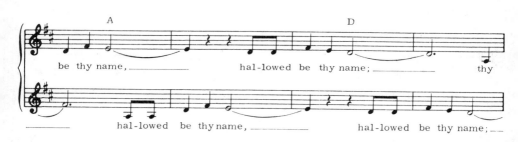

be thy name, _____ hal-lowed be thy name; _____ thy

_____ hal-lowed be thy name, _____ hal-lowed be thy name; __

king-dom come, _____ thy will be done _____ . up-

_____ thy king-dom come, _____ thy will be done _____

on the earth _____ as it is in heav'n. _____ Give

_____ up- on the earth _____ as it is in heav'n.

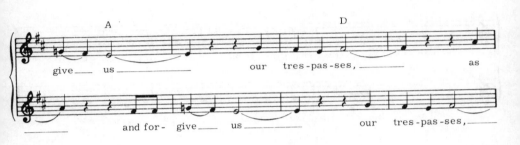

lead us not _____ in- to temp-ta-tion, _____ but de-

_____ and lead us not _____ in- to temp-ta-tion, _____

A   D

li- ver us _____ from ev- il. _____

_____ but de- li- ver us _____ from ev- il.

Doxology

D

For the king- dom, _____ the pow'r and the glory _____ are

For the king- dom, _____ the pow'r and the glory _____

A   D

yours, now _____ and for- ev-er. A-men. _____

_____ are yours, _ now _____ and for- ev-er. A-men.

INDEX OF FIRST LINES

This Index gives the first line of each hymn. If a hymn is known also by a title (e. g. Romans 8) this is given as well, but indented.

ACKNOWLEDGMENTS

The publishers wish to express their gratitude to the following for permission to use copyright material in this book:

The Church of the Messiah for The Lord is present in his sanctuary (2) ©1975 by Church of the Messiah, 231 East Grand Boulevard, Detroit, Michigan 48207, U.S.A. All rights reserved. Used by permission.

Maria Parkinson for As I kneel before you (7) ©1978 by the composer.

North American Liturgy Resources for Transfiguration (8) ©1977 by North American Liturgy Resources; You are near (23) ©1971, 1974 by Daniel L. Schutte; For you are my God (55) ©1970, 1974 by John B. Foley; Sing to the mountains (59) ©1975 by Robert J. Dufford and North American Liturgy Resources; If God is for us (64) ©1975 by John B. Foley and North American Liturgy Resources; Abba, Father (85) ©1977 by North American Liturgy Resources; Lay your hands (87) ©1977 by North American Liturgy Resources; Transfiguration (99) ©1977 by North American Liturgy Resources.

Shalom Community for Come, Lord Jesus (9) and Abba, Father (52) © Copyright 1974 by Shalom Community, 1504 Polk, Wichita Falls, TX 76309. All rights reserved. Used with permission.

Rev. Robert Stamps for God and man at table are sat down (10).

Celebration Services (International) Ltd for Allelu (11) ©1971, 1975; Fear not, rejoice and be glad (35) ©1971, 1975; I will sing, I will sing (68) ©1974, 1975; Please break this bread, Lord (77) ©1975; Hallelujah, My Father (96) ©1975. All rights reserved. Used by permission.

Word (UK) Ltd for Freely, freely (12) and Doxology (39) both from 'Come Together' by Jimmy and Carol Owens ©1972 Lexicon Music Inc. Used by permission. All rights reserved.

Joe Wise for Christ has died (17) and When we eat this bread (58).

Geoffrey Chapman, a division of Cassell Ltd, for Keep in mind (25); My soul is longing (80); All the earth proclaim the Lord (93). ©1965 World Library of Sacred Music, Inc.

Leonard E. Smith for Our God reigns (29) Copyright © by Leonard E. Smith, Jr., 225 Pine Mill Road, Clarksboro, N.J. 08020, U.S.A. Used by permission.

The Word of God, P.O. Box 8617, Ann Arbor, MI 48107, U.S.A. for I heard the Lord (30) ©1973, The Word of God. All rights reserved; The Light of Christ (60) ©1974, The Word of God. All rights reserved; Alleluia No. 1 ©1973, The Word of God. All rights reserved.

Editions du Chalet, 36 Rue de Trion, Lyon, France for All glory to you (Music only) (31); Sanctus of The Kintbury Mass (Music only) (16).

Sheed & Ward Ltd. for As long as men (42).

Editions Fleurus, 31 Rue de Fleurus, Paris 6e, France for In your coming and going (Music only) (46).